SPACE JUNK

Contents

Skateboard
Contest   2

Hi Alien   12

Space Junk   20

My Robot   26

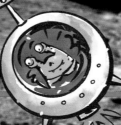

SKATEBOARD CONTEST

WRITTEN BY TRADEA SAND

ILLUSTRATED BY BRENT PUTZE

There was going to be a team skateboard contest.
Jed, Zack, Morgan and Maddie
were going to go in the contest.

"We have to get our tricks right," said Morgan.
"We have to get the handplant right.
We will win if we can do handplants."

Maddie went first.
She went up and down the ramp.
She got faster and faster.
At the top,
she put one hand on the ramp
and one hand on her skateboard.
Her legs went up and up and up.
And then Maddie and her skateboard
went zooming into space.

"Wow!" she said. "Where am I?"
She looked down.
She saw the park.

"Wow!" she said. "I'm up in space!"

Maddie zoomed on and on in space.
The sky was black. She saw lots of stars.
She saw the moon.

What do you think
a handplant is?
Why do you think the sky is
black in space? Don't turn over
until you know the answer.

3

"Wow!" said Maddie.
"I'm going to the moon."

And bump!
Maddie and her skateboard
landed on the moon.

"What am I going to do now?"
she said.

"Try out your handplants,"
said a little moon voice.
"You can do them on the moon."

Maddie tried out her handplant.
She tried it over and over and over.

"Wow!" she said.
"Now I can do a handplant!"

In the park, Jed and Zack
and Morgan were looking for Maddie.

"Where did she go?" said Jed.

"I'm here, I'm up here on the moon,"
called Maddie.

"Tell them to come up here too,"
said the little moon voice.

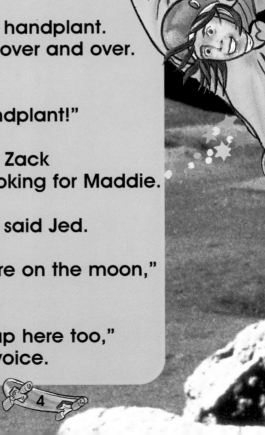

"How will they get here?" said Maddie.

"Like you did," said the little moon voice.
"Tell them how to do it."

"Come up here with me," called Maddie.

"How will we get there," called Morgan.

"Go up and down the ramp,"
called Maddie.
"At the top, put one hand on the ramp
and one hand on your skateboard.
Your legs will go up and up.
Then you will zoom up into space
and land on the moon."

Why do you think the
moon is a good place for
skateboard tricks?
What will happen next?
Will the others get
there too?

5

Zack and Jed and Morgan
went up and down the ramp.
They got faster and faster.
And then Zack and Jed and Morgan
and their skateboards
were zooming into space.

They zoomed on and on in space.
The sky was black. They saw lots of stars.
They saw the moon.

"Wow!" they said.
"We're going to land on the moon."

And bump!
They landed on the moon right by Maddie.

If this story was true, what would the children need to travel in space?

What would you call it if the children all tried to get to the moon first?

A space race!

"Look at me doing handplants," said Maddie.

"Wow!" said Jed. "You are good, Maddie."

"You try," said Maddie.
"You can do handplants on the moon."

7

Zack and Jed and Morgan tried and tried.
"You can all do handplants now,"
said the little moon voice.
"Go back now and win the skateboard contest."

"How will we get back?" said Maddie.

"Do a handplant at the same time.
Maddie and Morgan first.
Then Jed and Zack," said the little moon voice.

Maddie and Morgan and Jed and Zack
all did a handplant.
Their legs went up and up.
And then Maddie and Morgan
and their skateboards went zooming into space.

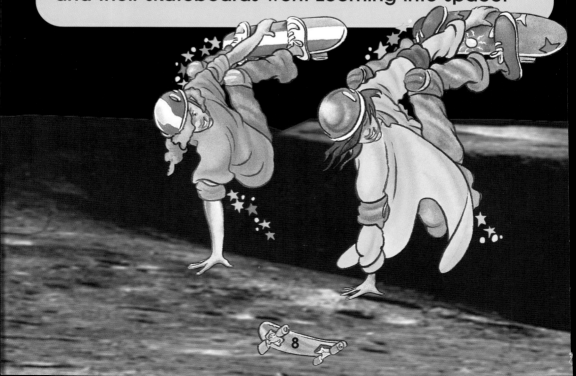

They zoomed on and on in space.
The sky was black. They saw lots and lots of stars.
They saw the earth.
They saw the skateboard ramp in the park.

"Wow!" they said.
"We're going to land in the park."

And bump!
They landed in the park
right by the skateboard ramp.

What will happen
next?
Will they win the
contest?

The skateboard contest was on.
The downtown team were on.
They went up and down the ramp.
Then one girl did a handplant.

"Look at that," said Zack.
"Two of us will have to do a handplant
at the same time.
Then we can win."

Maddie and Morgan were on.
They went up and down the ramp.
They got faster and faster.

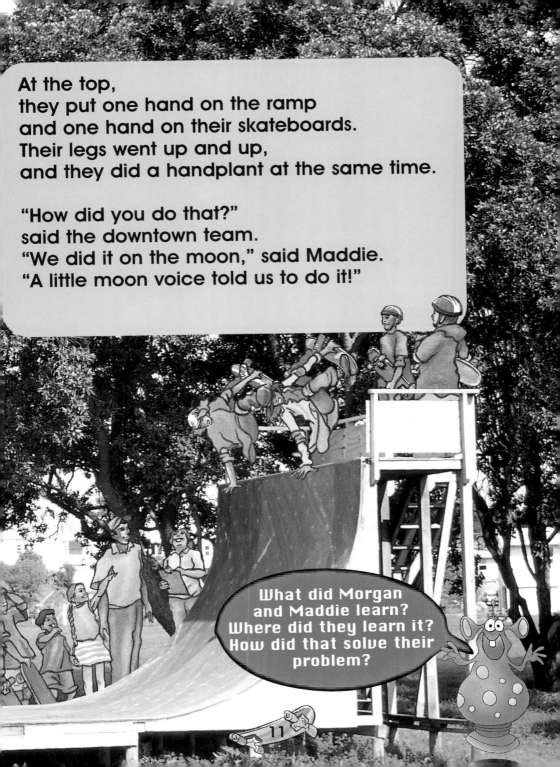

At the top,
they put one hand on the ramp
and one hand on their skateboards.
Their legs went up and up,
and they did a handplant at the same time.

"How did you do that?"
said the downtown team.
"We did it on the moon," said Maddie.
"A little moon voice told us to do it!"

What did Morgan and Maddie learn? Where did they learn it? How did that solve their problem?

11

Hi Alien

Written by Elizabeth McCabe
Illustrated by Nicola Belsham

To:Brad@penpal.com

Hi Brad

I am an alien.
I am looking for a pen pal.
Will you be my pen pal?
Will you send me
some e-mail?

Alien

Hi Brad

Thank you for your e-mail.
Yes, I will come to Earth.
Where will I find you?
I need a flat place
to land my spaceship.
Is there a flat place
by your house?

Alien

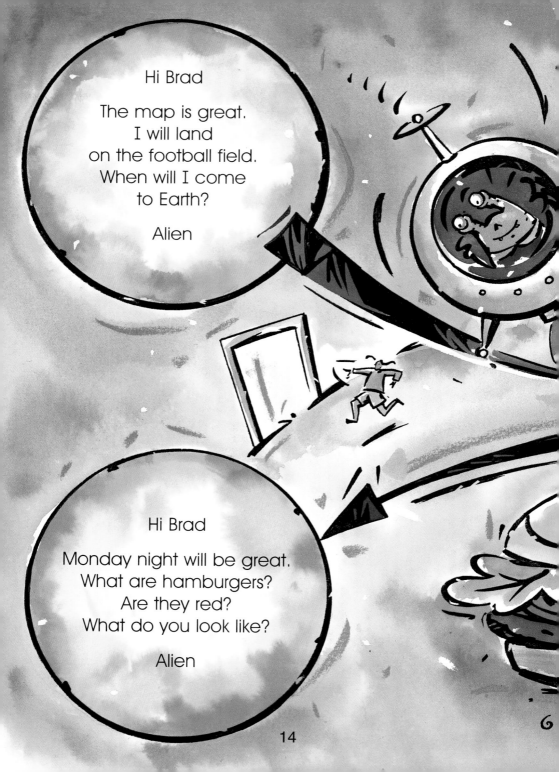

Hi Brad

I can look like lots of things.
The tall one is my pet!
I will come to your house
in a spaceship.

Alien

Space Junk

Written by Richard Gunther
Illustrated by Jim Storey

Space Sale

Al Jones went to a space sale. The space sale was on Saturday, May 10. Lots of people were at the space sale. Some people came to get spacesuits. Some people came to get space boots. Some people came to get space bags. Some people came to get space buggies. Some people came to get space junk. Al Jones came to look at the space junk. Al Jones liked the space junk so he got all of it.

"I did not want a spacesuit, or a space bag or a space buggy or space boots," said Al Jones. "They cost too much. So I got all the space junk."

Al Jones took the space junk home. He gave the space junk to his children to play with. They put on some of the space junk. They looked like space people. The children had fun with the space junk.

Space Sale
One day space sale!
On Saturday, May 10,
at Sally's Space Place.
Spacesuits, space boots,
space bags, space buggies
and space junk!
Come and look!

WILDCATS CHRONICLE

World A3

Sport A12

Entertainment C1

Motoring D4

Children Fly to the Moon

Leroy and Sandra Jones flew to the moon on Saturday, May 10. The children were playing with some space junk. They pulled a cord on some of the space junk and then they could fly. The children flew out of the window and down the road. They flew up over the town to the moon.

"We liked flying," said Sandra. "So we flew to the moon."

The two children went to a space sale on the moon. They saw a daddy moon-toggle get some space junk. The daddy moon-toggle gave the space junk to his moon-toggle children to play with. The children saw the moon-toggle children pull a cord on some space junk and then fly into the air.

Leroy and Sandra said they want to go back to the moon very soon.

Does a daddy moon-toggle look like me?

21

Toggle Times

| Moon A3 | Sport A12 | Entertainment C1 | Motoring D4 |

Space Sale

Daddy Moon-Toggle went to a space sale. The space sale was on Saturday, May 10. Lots of moon-toggles were at the space sale.

Some moon-toggles came to get spacesuits. Some moon-toggles came to get space boots. Some moon-toggles came to get space bags. Some moon-toggles came to get space buggies. Some moon-toggles came to get space junk. Daddy Moon-Toggle came to look at the space junk. Daddy Moon-Toggle liked the space junk so he got all of it.

"I did not want a spacesuit, or a space bag or a space buggy or space boots," said Daddy Moon-Toggle. "They cost too much. So I got all the space junk."

Daddy Moon-Toggle took the space junk home. He gave the space junk to his children to play with. They put on some of the space junk. They looked like space people. The children had fun with the space junk.

Space Sale
One day space sale!
On Saturday, May 10,
at Zarah's Space Place
Spacesuits, space boots,
space bags, space buggies and
space junk.
Come and look!

Toggle Times

| Moon A3 | Sport A12 | Entertainment C1 | Motoring D4 |

Moon-Toggles Fly to Earth

Two moon-toggle children flew to Earth on Saturday, May 10.

The children were playing with some space junk. They pulled a cord on some of the space junk and then they could fly.

The children flew out of the window and down the road. They flew up over the town to Earth.

"We liked flying," said Zora. "So we flew to Earth."

The two children went to a space sale on Earth. They saw an earth man get some moon junk. The earth man gave the space junk to his earth children to play with. The children saw the earth space junk and then fly into the air.

Zed and Zora said they want to go back to Earth very soon.

STOP!

Have you got a picture in your mind of Zarah's Space Place? What is real space junk?

WILDCATS CHRONICLE

World A3   Sport A12   Entertainment C1   Motoring D4

Alien Sighting

Today, Amy Brown said that she had seen two space children. The space children were at a space sale. Amy Brown had been to the space sale with Al Jones. Sandra and Leroy Jones were the children who played with the space junk. They were the children who flew to the moon.

Amy Brown said that the space children did not have on spacesuits or space boots. She looked for a spaceship but she could not see one. She did not know how the space children had got to the space sale at Sally's Space Place.

Leroy and Sandra Jones said that they had seen some moon toggle children when they were on the moon. They had seen the moon toggle children playing with some space junk. They had seen the moon toggle children take off into space. Leroy and Sandra said that the space children at Sally's Space Place could be the moon toggle children.

WILDCATS CHRONICLE

Space Junk

Space is very, very big. There are so many things in space. There are stars, moons and the sun. There are some things in space that should not be there. Space junk should not be in space.

Space junk flies around in space. Some space junk comes from rockets. Some space junk comes from spaceships. If you fly in space, you need to look out for it. Space junk can hit the window of a spaceship. Space junk can hit a spacesuit. It is not good to have space junk in space.

One day there will be a way to take all the space junk out of space. Then spaceships can fly in space and not have to look out for space junk.

Find out more about space junk. You could use the Internet to help you.

My Robot

My Robot was written by Glenis Knopp and Charles Young and photographed by Wendy Cook. Have fun making your own robot!

One day Charles made a robot. To make a robot you will need:

- one big box
- one little box
- two tubes

- two sticks
- a spark plug

- two big plastic tops
- two little bottle tops

- bolts and screws
- a block of wood
- glue and sticky tape
- paint and brushes
- scissors

- two bed springs
- two cups to fit in the bed springs

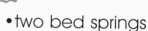

This is what I did.

I got two boxes.
A little box for the head
and a big box for the body.
I put the little box on top of the big box.
I stuck the two boxes with tape.
I put the tubes on the sides of the big box.
The tubes were the arms.
I stuck the arms on with tape.

STOP!

Is Charles's robot going to look like me?

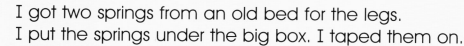

I got two springs from an old bed for the legs.
I put the springs under the big box. I taped them on.
The springs made the robot rock.
So I put two cups in the springs to stop them rocking.
I got some wood from a teacher.
I stuck the springs onto the wood with tape.
Now the robot did not rock.

What else could you make a robot out of?

28

My robot did not look like a robot.
I made it a face.
I got a spark plug for the nose.
I stuck the spark plug on.
I got bottle tops for the eyes.
I stuck on the bottle tops.
I got some wire mesh for the mouth.
I stuck the wire mesh on.
I got big plastic tops for the ears.
I taped the ears on.
I put the sticks into the top of the little box.
Now my robot looked like a robot.

I gave my robot some buttons.
I got bolts and screws for the buttons.
I stuck the bolts and screws on.
It was time to paint my robot.
I painted it yellow and blue.

My robot was too big to fit on the school bus.
My teacher put the robot in her car.
She took it to my house.
I made a big sign for the robot.
The sign had my robot's name on it.
I called my robot Henry!
Can you make a robot now?

My friend said I am a vain alien because I keep hoping people will look like me!

Glossary

🐾 **alien** – an imaginary creature from space that does not belong to Earth

🐾 **e-mail** – mail that is sent from one computer to another computer

🐾 **Internet** – a network that links computers so that people can share their ideas

🐾 **pen pal** – a friend made through letter writing

🐾 **skateboard ramp** – a ramp (bent at both ends) that is made for skateboarders to try out moves and tricks

🐾 **robot** – a machine invented to do tasks, in the way that a person would

🐾 **skateboard tricks** – tricks (such as wheelies, board jumps, and turns) made on a skateboard